This igloo book belongs to:

igloobooks

Published in 2017
by Igloo Books Ltd
Cottage Farm
Sywell
NN6 0BJ
www.igloobooks.com

Illustrated by Amanda Enright
Written by Stephanie Moss and Melanie Joyce

Cover designed by Lee Italiano
Interiors designed by Jason Shortland
Edited by Hannah Cather

LEO002 0317
2 4 6 8 10 9 7 5 3 1
ISBN 978-1-78670-927-1

Printed and manufactured in China

Magical Stories

igloobooks

I want to be a
Princess

I want to be a **princess.**
It would be a **dream** come true.

I'd live on a hill, in a **beautiful** castle,
with **cute** windows and purple flags, too.

My **pony** would live in the royal stables.
I'd visit him each day with a **treat.**

I'd bring him **lots** of juicy apples,
because they're what he **loves** to eat.

I'd invite all my princess **friends**
to come and have tea **parties** with me.

We'd eat **cakes,** strawberries, jelly and ice cream
for breakfast, lunch and **tea.**

One day, I'd meet a **handsome** prince
and there'd always be lots of **laughter.**

We'd have a magical royal **wedding**
and live **happily** ever after.

I want to be a
Ballerina

I want to be a **ballerina.**
I'd **dance** and twirl all day long.

I'd wear a beautiful **pink** tutu
and move **gracefully** to every song.

I'd put a **sparkling** tiara on my head
and tie my hair up with a **pretty** bow.

I'd own lots of skirts and **shiny** dresses,
and **special** outfits for every show.

I'd **always** dance my best on stage
and be given a **lovely** bunch of roses.

The audience would **clap** and cheer,
just before the curtain closes.

I want to be a
Fairy

I want to be a **fairy,**
who can **fly** high into the sky.

I'd **flutter** my little fairy wings,
just like a beautiful **butterfly.**

I'd have a pretty **magic** wand,
and I'd **wave** it here and there.

It would shimmer, shine and **sparkle,**
as I **swished** it though the air.

I'd share a picnic with all my **friends.**
We'd **giggle,** chat and play.

We'd eat **yummy** cakes and crunchy cookies,
and have fairy **fun**, all day.

I'd **always** carry a bag of fairy dust
that twinkled with **glitter** and light.

I'd cast all kinds of happy **spells.**
It would be the **most** wonderful sight!